The Elves and the Shoemaker

Retold by Margaret Nash

Illustrated by Anna C Leplar

Heinemann

Once upon a time there was a shoemaker
who had no leather to make his shoes.
He had no gold to buy more leather
so he shut up his shop and went home.

'What am I going to do?' he asked
his wife.

His wife put her arm in his arm.

'Something good will come,' she said.

'You will see.'

The next day the shoemaker and
his wife went to the shop.

4

The shoemaker opened the door
and stopped.

'Look!' he said to his wife. 'Do you
see what I see?'

'Shoes!' she said. 'I can see some shoes.'

5

The shoemaker looked at the heels.

Then he looked at the toes.

'They are good,' he said.

'They are as good as the shoes I make.

But who made them? Who?'

Just then an old man came into the shop.
'I would like to buy the black shoes,'
he said. 'Can I give you gold for them?'
'Yes you can, my good man,' said
the shoemaker. 'And thank you.'

So the shoemaker went to buy some leather with the gold.

He went back to his shop and cut out some more shoes.

Then he went home.

The next day the shoemaker and his
wife went to the shop. The shoemaker
opened the door and stopped.

'Look!' he said to his wife. 'Do you see
what I see?'

'Shoes!' she said. 'I can see more shoes.'

Just then a woman came into the shop.
'I would like to buy the red shoes,'
she said. 'Can I give you gold for them?'
'Yes you can, my good woman,' said
the shoemaker. 'And thank you.'

And so it went on, day after day …
The shoemaker went to buy more
leather. He cut out more shoes
and then he went home.

The next day he went back to the shop
and the shoes were made – lots and
lots of them.

Then one day the shoemaker said to
his wife, 'Now I have a big pot of gold
and lots of shoes, but I want to find out
who is making the shoes for me.'
'Let's find out tonight,' said his wife.
'We can hide under the table.'
And so they did.

That night as the shoemaker and
his wife hid under the table,
they saw two very little men.
The men jumped on to the table.
'Look!' said the shoemaker to his wife.
'Elves! And they are making the shoes.'

13

The next day the shoemaker said to
his wife, 'How can we thank the elves?'
'Let's make them some clothes,'
said his wife.

So the shoemaker and his
wife made some little
clothes for the elves.
They put them on the
table and they went home.

That night when the elves saw
the clothes they were very happy.
They put on the clothes and laughed
and jumped and danced about.
Then they ran off into the night
and didn't come back.

15

The shoemaker was happy too.
He had lots of gold to buy leather
and he could make his shoes again.
His wife put her arm in his arm.
'See!' she said. 'Something good did come!'